"Charles Schulz is the only man we know who can make a round circle, a dash, a loop and two black spots express the following: an abiding love for Beethoven, a disillusionment with all women or an eight-day crusade of hate against a paper kite.

"If Charlie Schulz jiggles the circle, spots, dash and loop one way a comic strip character named Charlie Brown will tear your heart out with man's inhumanity to man. If he wiggles them a little differently he will set you to laughing so hard your sides will ache.

"The ability to make these little ink scratches into facial expressions is, of course, the mark of the great cartoonist—and Charlie Schulz has been voted the greatest of them all by the National Cartoonists Society."

—*New York World Telegraph and Sun*

You're A Winner, Charlie Brown!

Selected Cartoons from GO FLY A KITE,
CHARLIE BROWN Vol. 1

Charles M. Schulz

CORONET BOOKS
Hodder Fawcett, London

First published by Fawcett Publications, Inc.,
New York 1966
Coronet edition 1967
Second impression 1967
Third impression 1968
Fourth impression 1968
Fifth impression 1969
Sixth impression 1970
Seventh impression 1971
Eighth impression 1973
Ninth impression 1973
Tenth impression 1974
Eleventh impression 1975

Printed and bound in Great Britain for
Coronet Books,
Hodder Fawcett,
St. Paul's House, Warwick Lane,
London, EC4P 4AH
by Hazell Watson & Viney Ltd,
Aylesbury, Bucks

ISBN 0 340 02709 6

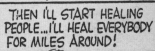

IN THE OLDEN DAYS THIS WAS KNOWN AS BRINGING THE WARRIOR HOME ON HIS SHIELD!

THESE ROCKS ARE ESPECIALLY GROOMED TO BE HURLED IN ANGER!

AFTER YOU'VE THROWN ALL OF THEM, DO YOU GO OUT AND PICK THEM UP?

OH, YES...I KEEP USING THE SAME ROCKS OVER AND OVER..

IT'S NOT UNLIKE RUNNING THEM THROUGH A FILTER!

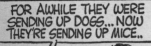

I'M GOING TO BE STAYING AT MY GRAMMA'S HOUSE FOR A FEW NIGHTS..

HOW COME, CHARLIE BROWN?

BECAUSE MY MOTHER WENT TO THE HOSPITAL LAST NIGHT..

MY DAD SAID SHE'LL BE ALL RIGHT...IN FACT, HE SAID SHE'LL BE HOME IN ABOUT FIVE DAYS..

FIVE DAYS? I WONDER... DO YOU SUPPOSE... I WONDER .IF...NO, IT COULDN'T BE... STILL...

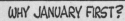

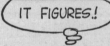

YOU'RE SO SWEET, SNOOPY.. I WISH I COULD GIVE YOU A BIG KISS, BUT OF COURSE, I CAN'T...

THE CURSE OF A FUZZY FACE!

HAVING A BABY SISTER HAS MADE A DIFFERENT PERSON OUT OF ME..

YOU JUST THINK IT HAS CHARLIE BROWN...YOU SEE, YOU'RE A "STATUS SEEKER"...

YOU JUST WANT SOMETHING THAT WILL BUILD YOU UP IN THE EYES OF THE OTHER KIDS IN THE NEIGHBORHOOD..

YOU COULD HAVE ACCOMPLISHED THE SAME THING WITH AN AUTOGRAPHED BASEBALL!

BOY, IT'S TOUGH TO BE A DOG WHEN IT RAINS!

OF COURSE, I'M LUCKIER THAN A LOT OF DOGS.... AT LEAST I HAVE A DOG HOUSE TO GO HOME TO...